The Church
Sacrament of Salvation

Student Workbook

– SEMESTER EDITION –

The Church
Sacrament of Salvation

Student Workbook

Midwest Theological Forum
Downers Grove, Illinois

Published in the United States of America by

Midwest Theological Forum
4340 Cross Street, Suite 1
Downers Grove, IL 60515
Tel (630) 541–8519
Fax (331) 777–5819
www.theologicalforum.org

General Editor:	Rev. James Socias
Editor-in-Chief:	Jeffrey Cole
Editorial Board:	Rev. James Socias, Rev. Peter Armenio, Scott Hahn, Ph.D., Jeffrey Cole
Other Contributors:	Gerald Korson, Randal Powers
Layout Design and Production:	Stephen J. Chojnicki, Kimberly D. Klotz

ISBN 978-1-936045-11-2

Contents

Abbreviations Used for the Books of the Bible

Gn	Genesis	Sir	Sirach	Acts	Acts of the Apostles
Ex	Exodus	Is	Isaiah	Rom	Romans
Lv	Leviticus	Jer	Jeremiah	1 Cor	1 Corinthians
Nm	Numbers	Lam	Lamentations	2 Cor	2 Corinthians
Dt	Deuteronomy	Bar	Baruch	Gal	Galatians
Jos	Joshua	Ez	Ezekiel	Eph	Ephesians
Jgs	Judges	Dn	Daniel	Phil	Philippians
Ru	Ruth	Hos	Hosea	Col	Colossians
1 Sm	1 Samuel	Jl	Joel	1 Thes	1 Thessalonians
2 Sm	2 Samuel	Am	Amos	2 Thes	2 Thessalonians
1 Kgs	1 Kings	Ob	Obadiah	1 Tm	1 Timothy
2 Kgs	2 Kings	Jon	Jonah	2 Tm	2 Timothy
1 Chr	1 Chronicles	Mi	Micah	Ti	Titus
2 Chr	2 Chronicles	Na	Nahum	Phlm	Philemon
Ezr	Ezra	Hb	Habakkuk	Heb	Hebrews
Neh	Nehemiah	Zep	Zephaniah	Jas	James
Tb	Tobit	Hg	Haggai	1 Pt	1 Peter
Jdt	Judith	Zec	Zechariah	2 Pt	2 Peter
Est	Esther	Mal	Malachi	1 Jn	1 John
Jb	Job	1 Mc	1 Maccabees	2 Jn	2 John
Ps	Psalms	2 Mc	2 Maccabees	3 Jn	3 John
Prv	Proverbs	Mt	Matthew	Jude	Jude
Eccl	Ecclesiastes	Mk	Mark	Rev	Revelation
Sg	Song of Songs	Lk	Luke		
Wis	Wisdom	Jn	John		

Chapter 1

GOD PREPARES THE WAY
FOR HIS CHURCH IN THE OLD TESTAMENT

INTRODUCTION

1. Explain this statement: Salvation history began with the sin of Adam and Eve.

2. What is the pivotal point of human history, and why?

3. What is the purpose of the Church?

4. What are some common names for the Church?

5. What is the source of the Church's life?

6. What kind of institution is the Church? How many natures does she have?

WE WERE MADE FOR COMMUNION WITH GOD

7. What does the text mean by this sentence: "We were made for communion with God"?

SIDEBAR: ST. IRENÆUS OF LYONS

8. What was St. Irenæus's major contribution to understanding the relationship among covenants of the Old Testament and with the New Covenant?

9. With which five figures of the Old Testament did God make his covenants?

THE COVENANT OF CREATION

10. As the creation narrative in Genesis recounts, after God had created Adam, he placed him in a garden and gave him the responsibility to take care of it. What lesson does this offer about the nature of human work?

11. Name, in order of appearance, the five books of the Pentateuch.

ADAM'S DISOBEDIENCE

12. What was the most important consequence of the Original Sin committed by Adam and Eve?

A PLAN FOR RESTORATION

13. What does the *Protoevangelium* have to do with salvation history?

14. How did the destruction of man's original relationship with God affect the relationship among human beings?

15. What does the narrative of Noah and the Ark reveal?

GOD CALLS ABRAM

16. What three promises did God make to Abraham, and what is their significance?

ABRAHAM, OUR FATHER IN FAITH

17. How did Abraham respond to God's promises? What can be learned from his response?

ABRAHAM'S OBEDIENCE

18. Comparing the story of Abraham and Isaac with the sacrifice of Jesus Christ, in what ways is Isaac a *type* (prefigurement) of Christ? To answer this question, complete the table below based on what you have learned in the chapter.

	Isaac	Jesus Christ
The father offers:		
The son submits:		
The sacrifice:		

A BLESSING FOR ALL NATIONS

19. God promised Abraham he would be a blessing for all nations. How did God ultimately fulfill this promise?

GOD CALLS MOSES

20. What name for himself did God reveal to Moses? What was the significance of God having revealed his name to Moses?

EXODUS FROM EGYPT

21. As God was preparing to send the tenth plague against Egypt because of the pharaoh's stubbornness in not setting free the people of Israel, he gave the Israelites instructions as to what they must do in order to be spared this fate. What was the name of this divinely revealed, annual feast, and what directions did God give the Israelites in order to spare their firstborn males?

22. Look ahead to the painting "Madonna and Child" (p. 31). Based on what you have learned about the lambs in the Books of Genesis and Exodus (cf. pp. 12, 15) and what you already know about the Redemption accomplished by Christ, why did Sesto depict the Christ child playing with a lamb?

23. During the Exodus, how did God protect and provide for his Chosen People? Why is this important?

GOD'S COVENANT WITH ISRAEL

24. In the covenant with Moses, what did God demand of the Israelites?

25. What was the Ark of the Covenant? Why was it important?

ISRAEL'S DISOBEDIENCE

26. While Moses was on Mount Sinai receiving the Law and Decalogue from God, what was going on among the Israelites in the desert below?

How did Moses react when he returned from the mountain to see the Golden Calf?

In response to the Golden Calf, what did God do with respect to the priesthood within Israel?

27. What were the consequences of Israel's disobedience, and how did God react to this disobedience?

28. To what sin were the Israelites especially prone?

ISRAEL DEMANDS A KING

29. Why did the Israelites demand God give them a king?

30. When God did give them a king, how was this king different from any other?

31. The Kings of Israel were anointed.
    What is the significance of the anointing of the kings of Israel?

    What are the Hebrew and Greek words for *anointed one*?

32. Review the illustrations "Saul Is Anointed King by Samuel" and "Anointing of David" (pp. 20–21). To *anoint* means to pour oil on a person; in many religious traditions, including Judaism and Christianity, it signifies a divine choice. Based on what you have learned about the anointing of King David (p. 21) and what you already know about the Sacrament of Confirmation instituted by Christ, how do the two correspond to each other?

33. Each of the kings of Israel had certain attributes or gifts to help him fulfill his kingly role. List the positive, kingly attributes of each of these kings:

Saul

David

Solomon

SIDEBAR: THE SEVEN PRIMARY FEATURES OF THE DAVIDIC COVENANT

34. List the seven primary features of the covenant God made with David.

a.

b.

c.

d.

e.

f.

g.

SIDEBAR: THREE ADDITIONAL FEATURES OR SECONDARY CHARACTERISTICS OF THE DAVIDIC COVENANT

35. Name the three secondary features of the Davidic Covenant.

    a.

    b.

    c.

THE REIGN OF SOLOMON AND THE COLLAPSE OF THE KINGDOM

36. What happened to Solomon's kingdom after his death?

37. What was the Northern Kingdom of Israel?

38. What was the role of the prophets?

39. This question requires thinking beyond the scope of the text. Some biblical critics and those opposed to the Jewish or Christian faiths are skeptical of much that appears in Scripture. By way of example, many people are skeptical of the plagues in Egypt recounted in the Book of Exodus. Such skeptics claim each of the plagues has a logical and natural explanation. For example, perhaps a normal infestation of flies could have spread a virus to the animals, or periodic swarms of locusts appeared in Egypt, sometimes in numbers so large they block the sunlight, both of which are said to explain two of the plagues in a single event. Even if all of the plagues could be explained naturally, what is a good way to answer these critics?

SUPPLEMENTARY READING

40. According to *Lumen Gentium*, how is the Church the New People of God, the New Israel (cf. *Supplementary Reading* 2, p.27)?

41. According to *Dei Verbum*, what does the Old Testament reveal (cf. *Supplementary Reading* 3, p.27)?

No Material on This Page

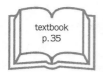

Chapter 2

JESUS CHRIST INSTITUTED THE CHURCH

PART I: GOD PREPARES HIS PEOPLE FOR THE CHURCH

1. In light of the Old Testaments covenants, what does the Church represent?

2. The first and second chapters discuss *typology*, a figurative and spiritual connection between people and events in the Old and New Testaments. In typology, the Old Testament person or event is called a *type*—sometimes called an *archetype*—of the corresponding person or event in the New Testament, which is called an *antitype*. In this way, the New Testament antitype is often a fulfillment, completion, or perfection of the Old Testament type.

   Complete the chart below using the appropriate antitype to complete the parallel between the Old and New Testaments.

Old Testament Type	New Testament Antitype

SIDEBAR: ST. AUGUSTINE

3. What was St. Augustine's great contribution to the study of Scripture?

THE INCARNATION

4. What is the Incarnation?

5. Explain the fourfold significance of the following quotation from St. Paul: "When the time had fully come, God sent forth his Son, born of woman . . . so that we might receive adoption as sons" (Gal 4:4).

   a.

   b.

   c.

   d.

THE PROCLAMATION OF THE KINGDOM OF GOD

6. What is the significance of Epiphany, the visit of the Magi to the infant Christ in Bethlehem?

7. What are the *synoptic* Gospels, and why is this adjective used?

8. How is the Kingdom of Heaven already present on earth?

9. What does it mean to say the Church is a *pilgrim* Church?

10. Why did Christ use parables to teach? Which of his parables are familiar to you?

11. What does the Parable of the Mustard Seed reveal about the Church?

JESUS CALLS THE TWELVE APOSTLES

12. Christ called together the Twelve Apostles to follow him in his ministry. Why is it significant for him to have called exactly *twelve*?

13. What role did the Apostles play in the early Church? How has this role continued, even to the present day?

SALVATION THROUGH THE CROSS

14. Why did St. John the Baptist refer to Christ as the Lamb of God?

SIDEBAR: WHAT DOES IT MEAN TO BE SAVED?

15. Christ is the Son of God, yet Christians are also sons and daughters of God by virtue of Baptism. Does this mean Christians are equal to Christ?

MADE KNOWN IN THE BREAKING OF THE BREAD

16. Explain the significance of the three meals Christ hosted in the Gospels.
    Feeding the five thousand:

    The Last Supper:

    The meal at Emmaus:

17. How has Christ continued to be present with his Church even to the present day?

THE FULFILLMENT OF THE OLD COVENANT IN THE CHURCH

18. Why are Christ and the Blessed Virgin Mary called the New Adam and the New Eve, respectively?

19. Review the painting "Lamentation" (p. 49), and then answer the following questions.

    What emotion does Solario express through the faces of the Blessed Virgin Mary and other characters?

    On a human level, why might they have expressed this emotion?

    On a spiritual level, why might they have expressed this emotion?

20. In the table below, fill in the blanks to indicate the role, form, and sign of each covenant listed.

Mediator	Role	Form	Sign
Adam			
	Father		
		Nation	
			Temple
Jesus			

A NEW AND EVERLASTING TEMPLE

21. What did Christ mean when he said, "Destroy this temple, and in three days I will raise it up"?

PART II: NAMES AND IMAGES OF THE CHURCH

22. How is the Church a mystery?

IMAGES OF THE CHURCH

23. What seven primary images are used to describe the Church in the New Testament?

THE MYSTICAL BODY OF CHRIST

24. What does it mean to say the Church is the Mystical Body of Christ?

25. Look ahead to the photograph of the papal Mass at the National Shrine of Our Lady of Aparecida (p.54). At large gatherings of Catholics, Masses are often concelebrated by bishops and priests, assisted by deacons, and attended by throngs of the faithful who are from different regions of the world and speak different languages. How does such a Mass express the truth of the Mystical Body of Christ?

SIDEBAR: THE CHURCH IS A "SHE"

26. Why is the Church given the feminine pronoun *she* rather than the neutral *it?*

SIDEBAR: THE CHURCH AS THE FAMILY OF GOD

27. How was the concept of family different in Christ's time than in the modern age?

THE FAMILY OF GOD

28. Each of the following is a way to know one is a child in the family of God. After each statement, describe how it is expressed in the Christian life.

   We live in God's house.

   We are called by his name.

   We eat at his table.

   We share his flesh and blood.

   His Bride is our Mother.

   We celebrate together.

   We receive instruction and discipline from him.

SIDEBAR: WORSHIPING AS THE NEW PEOPLE OF GOD

29. What is the difference between the worship of the People of God under the Old Covenant and their worship under the New Covenant? Explain how the Church today retains key elements of Jewish worship.

THE KINGDOM OF GOD

30. The seven primary features of God's covenant with David are listed below. After each feature, explain how it has taken on new meaning in the New Covenant in Christ.

    The covenant established a royal dynasty.

    The King of Israel was not only the son of David but also the son of God.

    The King of Israel was anointed.

    Mt. Zion was Israel's spiritual center.

    The Temple was the visible sign of the covenant and of God's kingdom.

The King of Israel was to rule over all the nations.

The thank offering was the primary sacrifice of the Temple.

textbook p. 75

Chapter 3

THE STORY OF THE EARLY CHURCH

INTRODUCTION

1. How did the Eleven Apostles spend their days after Christ's Ascension into Heaven?

"GO AND MAKE DISCIPLES OF ALL NATIONS"

2. What is the *Great Commission*, and what does it mean?

3. What did St. Peter establish as the requirement for a man to be a candidate to replace Judas in his Apostleship?

THE DAY OF PENTECOST

4. Answer the following questions about the first day of Pentecost.
   What are the signs of the presence of the Holy Spirit?

   What immediate effect did the Spirit have upon the Apostles?

   How effective was the Apostles' preaching?

   What does the word *Pentecost* mean, and what Jewish feast did it commemorate?

5. Review the painting "Pentecost" (p. 77). Identify the elements from St. Luke's account of the Descent of the Holy Spirit that are depicted in this painting (Acts 2:1–4; p. 79).

THE DESCENT OF THE HOLY SPIRIT

6. If Jesus is the *head* of the Mystical Body of Christ, the Church, then what can the Holy Spirit be considered to be?

7. List the six ways in which the Holy Spirit continues to work within the Church today, and briefly explain each.

   a.

   b.

   c.

   d.

   e.

   f.

ST. PETER'S AUTHORITY

8. Explain the primacy of St. Peter. Based on the Old Testament and the *Catechism*, what is the significance of Christ having given St. Peter the keys of the kingdom?

9. What is the significance of the power to bind and loose, which Christ also gave to St. Peter?

TRIALS AND PERSECUTION

10. Explain this quote from Tertullian (cf. CCC 853): "The blood of martyrs is the seed of Christians."

ST. PAUL, LIGHT FOR THE GENTILES

11. What was so dramatic about the conversion of Saul (later St. Paul)?

SIDEBAR: ST. PAUL, THE MAN CHOSEN FOR THE CONVERSION OF THE GENTILES

12. For what four reasons was St. Paul uniquely qualified to lead Christ's mission to the Gentiles?

    a.

    b.

    c.

    d.

PREACHING TO ALL NATIONS

13. What question about the Apostles' mission did St. Philip's encounter with the Ethiopian eunuch raise?

14. *This question requires a little more thought and perhaps some independent study.* Christ told the Apostles to teach all nations. Why was there even a question as to whether Gentiles should be baptized and whether they had to become Jews first?

15. What two things convinced St. Peter about the importance of taking the Gospel to the Gentiles and not to burden them with the Jewish Law?

16. What was decided at the Council of Jerusalem?

17. How was the primacy of St. Peter as the first pope evident in the Council of Jerusalem?

18. How was the missionary aspect of Christian discipleship apparent even at the beginning of Christ's public ministry when he called Sts. Peter, Andrew, James, and John?

ACTS OF THE APOSTLES

19. For each of the Twelve Apostles and St. Paul, fill in the appropriate information in each column below.

Name	Relatives among Apostles	Where he preached	Cause of Death
St. Peter			
St. James the Greater			
St. John			
St. Andrew			
St. Philip			
St. Bartholomew			
St. Matthew			
St. Thomas			
St. James the Lesser			
St. Jude			
St. Simon			
Judas Iscariot			
St. Paul			

20. When did Christ indicate to St. Peter he would have a unique role in the Church? What role did Christ promise to Peter?

21. What was unusual about the crucifixion of St. Peter?

22. Which came first, Sacred Scripture or Sacred Tradition, and how do you know?

23. What happened to St. John the Evangelist while he was in exile?

24. Of the five books of the New Testament written by St. John, which two are the longest? What is unique about each of these two books?

25. What is significant about Christ's calling of St. Matthew?

26. Search an art history book or the Internet for an image of Caravaggio's famous painting "The Calling of Saint Matthew," and then answer the following questions based on this painting and what you have learned about St. Matthew (p. 95; cf. Lk 5:27–28).

    What was St. Matthew doing when he was called by Christ?

    Given his profession, how was St. Matthew likely viewed by most of his contemporaries?

    The chief source of light is coming from the same direction as Christ and St. Peter. What might this suggest about the relationship between Christ and St. Matthew?

CALLED TO BE APOSTLES

27. How are people in the modern day to imitate the Apostles, and what is the apostolate?

"THY KINGDOM COME"

28. How did some Jews at the time of Christ conceive the promised Messiah? How did Christ differ from these expectations?

29. Christians speak of the Kingdom of God as being present on earth today but not yet in its fullness. Explain this, using as part of your answer the different stages of the coming of the Kingdom.

30. According to the Fathers of the Second Vatican Council (cf. *Lumen Gentium*, *Supplementary Reading* 3), how is the Church necessary for salvation?

name _____

Chapter 4

THE CHURCH AS
SACRAMENT OF SALVATION

THE CHURCH IS THE SACRAMENT OF SALVATION

1. How did the early Christians regard themselves, and how did they view the relationship between their community and the Jews?

2. According to the *Catechism*, no. 752, what are three meanings of the word *church*?

3. St. Paul called the union between Christ and his Church a *great mystery*. What does this mean?

THE MYSTERY OF THE CHURCH

4. Is the Church a visible society, an invisible society, or both? Explain.

5. What does it mean to say the Church is the Sacrament of Salvation?

THE CHURCH AS THE SACRAMENT OF COMMUNION

6. Match the proper dimension of the Church as *communion* with its definition below by writing the appropriate term on the line indicated.

horizontal   invisible   vertical   visible

a. _____ communion with God

b. _____ communion among the members of the Church

c. _____ communion with Trinity and the saints on earth, in Purgatory, and in Heaven

d. _____ communion in the teachings of the Church, the sacraments, and the hierarchical order

THE HIERARCHICAL STRUCTURE OF THE CHURCH

7. Briefly explain the structure of the Church hierarchy. How is this hierarchy different from any other hierarchical structure?

8. What is Apostolic Succession, and why is it so important?

9. Why is the Church not a democracy?

10. What is the Sacrament of Holy Orders?

SIDEBAR: HOW A POPE IS ELECTED

11. What is a cardinal of the Church?

12. Fill in the blanks below to complete the explanation of how a pope is elected.

    a. Between fifteen and twenty days after a pope dies, the _____ of the Church gather in what is called a _____.

    b. They assemble in the _____ and take an oath of secrecy. They cannot communicate with anyone on the outside until a new pope is elected. Those who have reached the age of _____ are not eligible to cast a vote.

    c. When a vote is taken, a _____ majority is required for election. If a vote results in no winner, the ballots are burnt, and chemicals are added to produce _____ smoke through the chimney, signaling to the faithful a decision has not been reached.

    d. When a vote results in a winner, the ballots are burnt and _____ smoke is produced, signaling a successful election. When the new pope accepts, he takes office immediately and chooses his name. Bells are rung, and the new pope is introduced to the crowd from the balcony. The new pope gives his papal blessing, which is called _____.

ST. PETER AND THE PAPACY

13. What is infallibility?

ROMAN CURIA

14. What is the Roman Curia?

THE OFFICE OF BISHOP

15. Review the painting "The Martyrdom of St. Ignatius" (p. 120). The elderly bishop St. Ignatius was eaten alive by lions as punishment for having proclaimed the Faith. Why do Christians celebrate this, even to the point of painting images of this very violent death? (Hint: The Greek *martyr* means *witness*.)

SIDEBAR: WHAT IS A CATHEDRAL?

16. Review the photograph of the *cathedra* of the Diocese of Rome (p. 121), and then answer the following questions about the *cathedra* of your own diocese. (If you belong to one of the Eastern Rites of the Catholic Church, the *cathedra* is called the *high place*; this is different than the bishop's chair on the *kliros*, or *kafedra*.)

    In what city is your bishop's *cathedra* located?

    What features—e.g., architecture, decoration, etc.—distinguish your bishop's *cathedra* from every other chair in the cathedral? (If you do not know what your bishop's *cathedra* looks like, search a diocesan historical record or the Internet for a photograph.)?

ECUMENICAL COUNCILS

17. Answer the following questions about the Ecumenical Councils of the Church.

    In what city was the first Ecumenical Council held, and in what year was it held?

    What question dominated the Ecumenical Councils of the first millennium?

    Which Ecumenical Councils do the Eastern Orthodox Churches recognize?

    What is the most recent Ecumenical Council, and when was it held?

    Who has the power to convene an Ecumenical Council?

THE OFFICE OF PRIEST

18. What does it mean to say *in persona Christi?*

SIDEBAR: WHAT IS A PARISH?

19. What is a parish?

THE OFFICE OF DEACON

20. Explain the difference between a *transitional* deacon and a *permanent* deacon.

THE TEACHING AUTHORITY OF THE CHURCH

21. What is the Deposit of Faith?

22. What are Sacred Tradition and Sacred Scripture? What is their relationship?

THE DEPOSIT OF FAITH

23. What are the three stages in the formation of the Gospels?

THE MAGISTERIUM

24. What is the distinction between the *ordinary* and *extraordinary* Magisterium?

25. What is the difference between *obedience of faith* and *religious assent*?

SANCTIFYING AND GOVERNING ROLE OF THE CHURCH

26. According to the *Catechism of the Catholic Church*, what are the three main responsibilities of the diocesan bishop?

27. How do bishops sanctify the faithful?

PRECEPTS OF THE CHURCH

28. What do the Precepts of the Church require of the faithful?

SALVATION AND THE CHURCH

29. Outside the Church there is no salvation. Does this mean only Catholics can be saved? Does it mean only Christians are saved? Explain.

ECUMENICAL AND INTERFAITH RELATIONS

30. If non-Catholic Christians are part of the Body of Christ and can be saved without formally becoming Catholic, then why bother with ecumenism or trying to draw them to Catholicism?

31. If salvation outside the Church is possible, why does the Church bother to evangelize people, to preach the Gospel to people of other faiths?

31. Review the photograph of Pope Benedict XVI in Bethlehem (p. 132) and the paragraph "Among the other..." (p. 133).

32. In addition to acknowledging there is only one God, what great similarity exists between the beliefs of Catholics and Muslims?

SUPPLEMENTARY READING

33. According to the Fathers of the Second Vatican Council (*Lumen Gentium, Supplementary Reading* 2), can an individual bishop teach infallibly? When can a bishop teach infallibly?

34. According to Pope Benedict XVI (*Supplementary Reading* 4), what is the purpose of interfaith dialogue? What message did he convey to the Jewish and Muslim communities?

35. Take a moment to reflect on your membership in the Church. Describe the ways in which you form part of the visible and invisible Church. How can you participate in the Church and her work of bringing salvation to mankind? (N.B. Non-Catholics and Catholics alike can answer this question.)

textbook
p.145

name _____

THE FOUR MARKS OF THE CHURCH: ONE, HOLY, CATHOLIC, AND APOSTOLIC

INTRODUCTION

1. What are the four marks of the Church?

2. From whom does the Church receive these four marks?

3. What is the purpose of the four marks of the Church?

THE FIRST MARK: THE CHURCH IS ONE

4. At what point in the Mass are the four marks of the Church reaffirmed?

UNITY IN THE MYSTICAL BODY

5. How does the famous image of the Mystical Body of Christ illustrate the unity, or oneness, of the Church?

6. When Adam and Eve sinned, they damaged their relationship with God and with each other. Why, then, is the unity, or oneness, of the Church an integral part of the New Covenant established by Jesus Christ?

7. What three expressions of the Church's unity, or oneness, are visible in the Mystical Body of Christ?

SIDEBAR: POPE ST. LEO THE GREAT

8. Pope St. Leo the Great battled the heresies of the fifth century with considerable success, but one of his most famous battles took place against the marauding barbarian Attila the Hun. What happened between these two?

WOUNDS TO UNITY

9. Identify each of the following as examples of apostasy, heresy, or schism.

   a. _____ A Catholic college professor has taught for years he believes Christ did not literally rise from the dead but the Resurrection is a metaphor to express how the Apostles felt Christ's presence among them even after death.

   b. _____ Upset over a bishop's plan to close their parish and consolidate it with a neighboring parish, a group barricades itself inside the Church in protest and, despite warnings from the bishop about excommunication, eventually hires its own priest to provide liturgical services.

   c. _____ Molly, influenced by the views of an atheistic friend, decides she can't believe in Christ anymore and stops going to church entirely.

10. The mark of unity, or oneness, is a gift from God. What, then, is the source of apostasy, schism, and heresy?

11. Explain the distinction between *schismatics* and *separated brethren*.

12. What do the Catholic Church, Orthodox Churches, and Protestant communities have in common, and why are these things important?

HERESIES IN THE EARLY CHURCH

13. What five major heresies troubled the early Church by challenging the orthodox understanding of the Person and natures of Christ?

14. Why were the early heresies especially dangerous to the Church?

15. How did the early Church defeat these heresies?

16. What does *Theotokos* mean? When was the title *Theotokos* solemnly defined by the Church? Which heretical group rejected this title?

17. What are the three general beliefs of Gnostics?

18. Who is the hero in defeating the Monophysite heresy, and how did he do this?

THE PROTESTANT REFORMATION

19. What is an indulgence, and what role did indulgences play in the Protestant Reformation?

20. After the first Protestant reformers had split from the Catholic Church in the sixteenth century, they found lasting stability and unity in the new Christian churches they founded. Is this statement true? Why or why not?

TOWARD GREATER CHRISTIAN UNITY

21. What are the four principles for ecumenical work as laid out by the Second Vatican Council's *Decree on Ecumenism*?

   a. The first principle:

   b. The second principle:

   c. The third principle:

   d. The fourth principle:

SIDEBAR: CONTEMPORARY EFFORTS
IN ECUMENISM AND INTERFAITH DIALOGUE

22. What efforts has the Church made recently to foster ecumenism and interfaith dialogue?

23. What are some obstacles to these efforts with the Orthodox Churches and Protestant communities?

24. Why is it important to persevere in ecumenical and interfaith dialogues?

THE SECOND MARK: THE CHURCH IS HOLY

25. Review the painting "St. Augustine and St. Monica" (p. 159) Read a short biography of St. Monica, and then answer the following questions.

Why is St. Monica an example of a life of prayer?

How did Scheffer depict St. Monica's life of prayer by the position of her and her son's hands and eyes?

26. Why is the Church holy?

27. What does the existence of saints in Heaven reveal about the holiness of the Church?

PARTICIPATION IN THE HOLINESS OF CHRIST

28. How does the Church already share in the bodily Resurrection of Jesus Christ?

THE CHURCH WILL RECEIVE HER PERFECTION IN THE GLORY OF HEAVEN

29. What three characteristics of perfection does the Church possess as a result of her divine origin?

THE THIRD MARK: THE CHURCH IS CATHOLIC

30. In what two ways can the Church be said to be *catholic*?

SIDEBAR: WHY DOES THE CHURCH HAVE DIFFERENT RITES?

31. Many Catholics might be surprised to learn there are twenty-one different rites in the Church. The rite with which most Catholics are familiar is the Latin, or Roman, Rite, but there are a number of Eastern Rites of the Catholic Church that recognize the authority of the pope and worship according to their deep roots in Church history, dating to the early churches in the Eastern Roman Empire, including Alexandria, Antioch, and Byzantium.

    Is a member of the Latin Rite of the Catholic Church allowed to attend Mass and receive the Eucharist at a church of one of the Eastern Rites of the Catholic Church?

    Is a member of one of the Eastern Rites of the Catholic Church allowed to attend Mass and receive the Eucharist at a church of the Latin Rite of the Catholic Church?

32. For each of the following Eastern Rites of the Catholic Church, state the early rite from which it originates.   *Alexandrian*   *Antiochene*   *Byzantine*

a. _____ Ukrainian Rite of the Catholic Church

b. _____ Greek Rite of the Catholic Church

c. _____ Malankar Rite of the Catholic Church

d. _____ Coptic Rite of the Catholic Church

e. _____ Syrian Rite of the Catholic Church

f. _____ Russian Rite of the Catholic Church

g. _____ Maronite Rite of the Catholic Church

h. _____ Slovak Rite of the Catholic Church

THE FOURTH MARK: THE CHURCH IS APOSTOLIC

33. In what three senses is the Church founded on the Apostles?

34. Each of the statements below supports one of the marks of the Church. Write the name of the mark each statement affirms: one   holy   catholic   apostolic

a. _____ Jesus Christ himself founded the Church.

b. _____ Every person is called to join the People of God.

c. _____ The Church teaches the unique, true religion.

d. _____ In the Church, sinners are enabled to become saints.

e. _____ The Church guards and transmits the teachings of the Apostles.

f. _____ The pope traces his authority back to St. Peter and Christ.

g. _____ The Church transcends all human boundaries.

h. _____ In the Eucharist, the faithful participate in the glory of Heaven.

35. Review the photograph of Pope Benedict XVI ordaining Bishop Giorgio Corbellini (p. 166). Pope Benedict received the power to ordain a bishop from the Holy Spirit when he was ordained a bishop in 1977 by Bishop Stangl, who was ordained a bishop in 1957 by Archbishop Schneider, who was ordained a bishop in 1955 by Cardinal Wendel, who was ordained a bishop in 1941 by Bishop Sebastian, who was ordained a bishop in 1917 by Archbishop Von Hauck. According to your text, how far back does this line of ordinations go, and to whom?

SUPPLEMENTARY READING

36. According to St. John Paul II (cf. *Supplementary Reading* 4), why is it important to be in a state of grace when receiving the Sacrament of the Eucharist?

No Material on This Page

textbook
p.177

Chapter 6

THE CHURCH IN THE LIFE OF THE FAITHFUL

INTRODUCTION

1. What is the main obstacle to living a truly Christian life, and how can this obstacle be overcome?

2. Review the paintings "The Baptism of Christ" and "Adoration of the Lamb" and look ahead to the photograph "Ecce Agnus Dei" (pp. 179, 187, and 200). Read the narrative of St. John's ministry of baptism (Jn 1:19–37), and then answer the following questions.

   As Christ was coming to St. John the Baptist to be baptized, what title did St. John cry (cf. Jn 1) out upon seeing the Messiah?

   Before the distribution of Holy Communion, the celebrant shows the faithful a consecrated host. What does he tell them to behold?

   What is the difference between Christ's presence in John 1:29 and his Real Presence in the Eucharistic species?

THE CHURCH IS THE PEOPLE OF GOD

3. Throughout the text, the Church has been presented in many ways, using many models and contexts. What title did the Fathers of the Second Vatican Council use predominantly to describe the Church?

4. Did the Fathers of the Second Vatican Council coin the title in the previous question? Explain.

5. How does the title in the previous two questions relate to another title for the Church—the *Mystical Body of Christ*—which was also used by the Council Fathers in the documents of Vatican II?

6. How does the title in Questions 2 and 3 relate to the title *Pilgrim Church*, yet another term used by the Council Fathers in the documents of Vatican II?

COMMON PRIESTHOOD OF THE FAITHFUL

7. St. Peter referred to the Church as a *royal priesthood*. Does this mean every one of the faithful is a priest?

8. Describe the differences and similarities between the common priesthood of the faithful and the ministerial priesthood.

9. Review the photograph of a teacher and student on page 184 of the text and the corporal and spiritual works of mercy (see the *Catholic Prayers and Devotions* section of this workbook), and then answer the following questions.

Which of the spiritual works of mercy does this photograph depict?

Which two of the corporal works of mercy do you recognize having practiced within the last few days, and how did you practice each one? (Be vague enough to protect others' privacy.) If you cannot recall having practiced these, answer with what you plan to do in the near future.

Which two of the spiritual works of mercy do you recognize having practiced within the last few days, and how did you practice each one? (Be vague enough to protect others' privacy.) If you cannot recall having practiced these recently, answer with what you plan to do in the near future.

UNIVERSAL CALL TO HOLINESS

10. What is the *universal call to holiness*?

11. What are the six proper responses to the universal call to holiness listed in the text?

    a.

    b.

    c.

    d.

    e.

    f.

THE LITURGICAL YEAR

12. What are the six seasons, or periods, of the liturgical year in the Ordinary Form of the Latin Rite?

    a.

    b.

    c.

    d.

    e.

    f.

THE SEVEN SACRAMENTS

13. What are the three purposes of the sacraments?

    a.

    b.

    c.

14. Why are the sacraments called *sacraments of faith*?

15. What does it mean to say a sacrament is *efficacious*? What Latin phrase does the Church use to describe this aspect of each sacrament?

16. Think about the following question for a few moments before giving an answer.

    It took the Church many centuries to formally define the sacraments as seven in number and which seven they are. The official list of seven was solemnly defined as a matter of the Faith at the Council of Trent in 1547.

    If the Seven Sacraments were all instituted by Christ, why did the Church not solemnly define this until 1547?

17. Why did Christ institute sacraments? Can he not give grace any way he pleases?

18. List the Seven Sacraments.

    a.

    b.

    c.

    d.

    e.

    f.

    g.

BAPTISM

19. What was the substantial difference, if any, between the baptism administered by St. John the Baptist and the Baptism instituted by Christ?

20. Answer the following questions about the Seven Sacraments.
    Which are the Sacraments of Initiation?

    Which sacraments leave an indelible character, or seal, and thus can only be received once?

    Which sacraments does the Church recommend the faithful receive frequently?

    Of which sacraments is the bishop the ordinary minister?

    In which sacrament are the recipients also the ordinary ministers?

21. Answer the following questions about the Sacrament of Baptism.
    What is the primary sign of Baptism?

What other signs and symbols appear in the celebration of Baptism?

22. Explain what is meant by *baptism of blood* and *baptism of desire*.

23. What happens to unbaptized babies, who can neither die for their faith nor desire Baptism? Do they go to Limbo but are denied the Beatific Vision of Heaven?

SIDEBAR: BAPTISM: THE DOORWAY OF THE CHURCH

24. Why is Baptism called the *Doorway of the Church*?

CONFIRMATION

25. How does the Sacrament of Confirmation get its name?

26. Why does the ordinary practice of the Latin Rite of the Catholic Church separate the Sacraments of Initiation by several years?

27. How does the practice of the Eastern Rites of the Catholic Church keep Baptism and Confirmation together?

EUCHARIST

28. Name two events, one in each of the Old and New Testaments, that foreshadow the Eucharist.

    a.

    b.

29. Answer the following questions about the Sacrament of the Eucharist.
    What does it mean to say the bread and wine become the Body and Blood of Christ?

    What word is used to describe what takes place at the consecration?

    How does the Church describe the presence of Christ in the Eucharist in his Body and Blood, Soul and Divinity?

30. How does attending Mass and receiving the Eucharist worthily benefit the recipient?

31. What does it mean to receive the Eucharist *worthily?*

PENANCE

32. What are two common, alternative names for the Sacrament of Penance?

33. Briefly define the following terms as they relate to rite of the Sacrament of Penance.
    Confession

    Contrition

    Penance

    Absolution

34. Review the stained-glass window of St. John Nepomucene (p. 204), and then read a short biography of him. Answer the following questions.
    Why is St. John Nepomucene called the martyr of the confessional?

    Why is St. John Nepomucene depicted with his finger over his lips?

ANOINTING OF THE SICK

35. Comment on this statement: The Sacrament of the Anointing of the Sick is for people who are about to die.

HOLY ORDERS

36. What are the three characters of ecclesial ministry exercised through the Sacrament of Holy Orders? Explain briefly what each one is.

    a.

    b.

    c.

MATRIMONY

37. How is the Sacrament of Matrimony a *vocation of service*?

TYPES OF PRAYER

38. What are the four main types of prayer?

    a.

    b.

    c.

    d.

39. Answer the following questions about prayer.
    What is a novena?

    What is *lectio divina*?

    What are the Stations of the Cross?

    What is the *ultimate prayer* of the Church?

40. What is the difference between a sacrament and a sacramental?

SACRIFICE AND SELF-DENIAL

41. Mortification and self-denial are means of growing in holiness. It can be practiced frequently, even in ordinary activities; the text lists several examples. List at least two examples of mortification and self-denial that could be performed in each of the situations listed.

    Dining with your family at a restaurant

    Sitting through a boring class lecture

    Taking a shower at home

    Washing dishes after a family meal

Driving in slow traffic

Suffering an illness or injury

SIDEBAR: THE ROLE OF YOUTH IN THE CHURCH

42. Review the photograph of a Palm Sunday procession (p. 218), and then answer the following questions.

    How are processions and parades used in secular culture?

    How was Christ's Entrance into Jerusalem (cf. Mt 21:8–11) similar to processions and parades in secular culture?

LIVING WITNESSES OF JESUS CHRIST

43. By what primary means can a person in the lay state participate in the missionary activity of the Church?

44. What strength is essential to be a living witness to Christ?

LIVING OUR FAITH IN THE MIDST OF THE WORLD

45. What does it mean for the laity to be involved in the *public square*?

46. Answer the following questions about the *common good*.
    What is the common good?

    What are the three essential elements of the common good?

    a.

    b.

    c.

VOCATION TO THE CONSECRATED LIFE

47. What are the evangelical counsels, and who primarily practices them?

TYPES OF CONSECRATED LIFE

48. What are the three main types of consecrated life?

    a.

    b.

    c.

name _____

Chapter 7

THE CHURCH AS A COMMUNION OF SAINTS

INTRODUCTION

1. In what prayer of the Rosary is the Communion of Saints explicitly affirmed?

THE CHURCH AS A COMMUNION OF SAINTS

2. What are the three states of being within the Communion of Saints? Briefly describe each.

   a.

   b.

   c.

3. How is each of the baptized a member of the Communion of Saints? Be sure to include the Church Militant, Church Suffering, and the Church Triumphant in your response.

SIDEBAR: WHAT IS AN INDULGENCE?

4. Answer the following questions about indulgences.
   What is an indulgence?

   How is an indulgence obtained?

   What is the difference between a *partial* indulgence and a *plenary* indulgence?

WHAT DOES IT MEAN TO BE A SAINT?

5. When does a person enter into the Communion of Saints?

6. What does it mean to say a person is *canonized*?

7. What do the lives of the saints, who are now in Heaven, reveal about the pursuit of holiness?

INTERCESSION OF SAINTS

8. What is the *intercession of the saints*?

9. How can a person on earth intercede for others?

10. Why should a person make intercessory prayers for others?

11. What evidence can be found in the Bible for the intercession of the saints?

12. Why did St. Dominic say, "Do not weep, for I shall be more useful to you after my death and I shall help you then more effectively than during my life," and why did St. Therese say, "I want to spend my heaven in doing good on earth"?

THE END OF HISTORY: A NEW HEAVEN AND A NEW EARTH

13. When will the end of the world come?

14. What four things are known about the end of the world?

a.

b.

c.

d.

15. Review the paintings "Last Judgment" and "The Last Judgment" (pp. 250–251); look ahead to the paintings "Christ Pantocrator and the Last Judgment" and "Hell" (pp. 254, 256); and then answer the following questions.

    In Michelangelo's painting and the icon in Florence, the right hand of Christ is positioned upward and his left hand positioned downward. Which of Christ's parables does this represent (cf. Mt 24)?

    At the top of Memling's painting the banner reads in Latin, "*In inferno nulla est redemptio*" ("In the fire [of Hell] there is no redemption"). In what ways does the icon in Florence show the glory of Christ's Redemption and salvation of his people?

16. Answer the following questions about persecution of and within the Church.

    Will the Church undergo persecution only at the end of time?

    How should Christians regard persecution?

ST. JOHN'S VISION OF THE HEAVENLY LITURGY

17. Is the Book of Revelation a retelling of events past, a foretelling of events in the future, or a depiction of the liturgy in Heaven?

18. Who is the High Priest of the heavenly liturgy? Who is the sacrificial Victim? What kind of sacrifice is the heavenly liturgy?

THE HOLY MASS IS A PARTICIPATION IN THE HEAVENLY LITURGY

19. What elements of the Mass correspond to the descriptions of the heavenly liturgy in the Book of Revelation?

20. What does it mean to say the Mass on earth is a participation in the heavenly liturgy?

THE LAST THINGS

21. What are the *Last Things*?

PARTICULAR JUDGMENT

22. What is the Particular Judgment?

SIDEBAR: WHY PRAY FOR THE DEAD?

23. What evidence in Scripture points to the acceptability and value of praying for the dead?

PURGATORY

24. The Fathers of the Church and theologians have described Purgatory as a state of great pain and yet a place of joy. How is this possible?

25. Who are the holy souls? What role do they play in intercession?

26. The Church regards praying for the dead to be a pious duty and a work of mercy. What three virtues oblige the faithful to pray for the dead?

    a.

    b.

    c.

HELL

27. How can an all-good, loving, and merciful God send a person, no matter how evil, to eternal damnation?

HEAVEN

28. Of what does the essential happiness of Heaven consist?

THE PAROUSIA

29. Answer the following questions about the *Parousia*.

    What is the *Parousia*?

    In the context of salvation history, what is the significance of *Parousia*?

30. What is the Last Judgment?

SIDEBAR: ST. MICHAEL THE ARCHANGEL

31. What three archangels are mentioned by name in Scripture?

    a.

    b.

    c.

CONCLUSION

32. Comment on this statement from the Conclusion and explain what it means for the life and vocation of the Christian: "We were not made for this earth, but for Heaven."

33. Look ahead to the painting of St. Elizabeth of Hungary (p. 264), and then read a short biography of her. Though she is depicted giving food to the poor, why is St. Elizabeth wearing fine clothes.

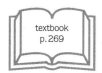
Chapter 8

MARY, MOTHER OF THE CHURCH AND OUR MOTHER

INTRODUCTION

1. Review the painting "Annunciation" (p. 271), and then answer the following questions. The answers can be found in St. Luke's account of this encounter (1:26–38).

   The Archangel Gabriel holds a white lily, which symbolizes the purity of the Blessed Virgin Mary. Which statement of his might this represent?

   The Archangel Gabriel points upward, as if to God. Which statement of his might this represent?

   The Blessed Virgin Mary has her head bowed and is showing her right palm. Which statement of hers might this represent?

   Why do you think it is okay for there to be more than one correct answer to these questions?

MARY IN GOD'S PLAN OF SALVATION

2. When did God the Father choose the Blessed Virgin Mary to be the Mother of his divine Son?

MOTHER OF GOD

3. What does it mean to say the Blessed Virgin Mary is the Mother of God?

4. Discuss the Blessed Virgin Mary's title of *Theotokos* in the context of Christ's divine identity as the Word of God.

SIDEBAR: CHURCH DOGMAS ABOUT MARY

5. The Church has made four solemn doctrinal definitions to explain certain aspects of the Blessed Virgin Mary's role in salvation history. Briefly explain each one, including when it was solemnly defined and by whom.

    Her Divine Maternity, or Motherhood:

    Her Perpetual Virginity:

    The Immaculate Conception:

    Her Assumption:

THE IMMACULATE CONCEPTION

9. Explain the significance of the Archangel Gabriel's greeting to the Blessed Virgin Mary at the Annunciation: "Hail, full of grace, the Lord is with you!" (Lk 1:28).

7. What does the Immaculate Conception reveal about the importance of grace in the lives of every Christian?

8. Answer the following questions about the New Eve and the New Adam.

   How is the Blessed Virgin Mary the *New Eve*?

   How is Christ the *New Adam*?

SIDEBAR: THE WOMAN OF THE *PROTOEVANGELIUM*

9. When is the Blessed Virgin Mary first referenced in salvation history?

THE ASSUMPTION OF THE BLESSED VIRGIN MARY

10. What is the relationship between the Blessed Virgin Mary's Assumption and Christ's Resurrection?

11. What does the Blessed Virgin Mary's Assumption reveal about the Church?

SIDEBAR: ST. JOSEPH

12. Answer the following questions about St. Joseph.

   Who was St. Joseph?

   What can be learned from St. Joseph's life?

THE PERPETUAL VIRGINITY OF MARY

13. In addition to Christ's divine nature, what does the Blessed Virgin Mary's Perpetual Virginity reveal?

SIDEBAR: DID JESUS HAVE BROTHERS AND SISTERS?

14. The Gospels refer to the *brothers of Jesus*. How, then, can the Blessed Virgin Mary have remained a virgin throughout her life?

MARY, MOTHER OF THE CHURCH

15. What does it mean to say the Church was born from Christ's side? (Hint: Adam's wife, Eve, was formed from his side.)

16. Answer the following questions about the Blessed Virgin Mary's role in the Church.

    What is the relationship between the Blessed Virgin Mary, Jesus Christ, and the Church?

    How is the Blessed Virgin Mary the Mother of the Church?

17. Answer the following two questions about the *woman*.

    In light of the Gospel, who is the *woman* in the *Protoevangelium*?

    What is the connection between the *woman* in the *Protoevangelium* and Christ's command to St. John, "Behold, your mother!" (Jn 19:27), during his Crucifixion?

SIDEBAR: "BEHOLD, YOUR MOTHER!"

18. Review in detail the painting "What Our Lord Saw from the Cross" (p. 282). For most of art history, a third-party (or "onlooker") perspective has dominated painting, but Tissot painted at a time when many artists began to utilize the perspective of a principal character in the scene, whether over the shoulder or from the viewpoint of the main character. What power do you think this painting has that would have been lacking had it been painted from a third-party perspective?

MARY, HELP OF CHRISTIANS

19. Answer the following questions about developing a relationship with the Mother of all Christians. Why is important to develop a personal relationship with the Blessed Virgin Mary?

   How can a Christian develop a personal relationship with the Blessed Virgin Mary?

MARY, MOTHER OF THE CHURCH

20. What is the Blessed Virgin Mary's relationship with other human beings?

SUPPLEMENTARY READING

21. According to St. John Paul II (cf. *Supplementary Reading* 1), what can the *Magnificat* teach about a proper attitude toward the Eucharist?

22. According to the Fathers of the Second Ecumenical Council of the Vatican (cf. *Lumen Gentium*, p. 288 of the text), what unique relationship does the Blessed Virgin Mary enjoy with the Blessed Trinity?

CATHOLIC PRAYERS AND DEVOTIONS

In any endeavor, there are certain basics that must be learned, memorized, and internalized. These prayers and devotions are fundamental to the life of an active, practicing Catholic.

The Ten Commandments

1. I am the LORD your God: you shall not have strange gods before me.
2. You shall not take the name of the LORD your God in vain.
3. Remember to keep holy the LORD's Day.
4. Honor your father and your mother.
5. You shall not kill.
6. You shall not commit adultery.
7. You shall not steal.
8. You shall not bear false witness against your neighbor.
9. You shall not covet your neighbor's wife.
10. You shall not covet your neighbor's goods.

The Precepts of the Church   (CCC 2042–2043)

1. You shall attend Mass on Sundays and holy days of obligation and rest from servile labor.
2. You shall confess your sins at least once a year.
3. You shall receive the sacrament of the Eucharist at least during the Easter season.
4. You shall observe the days of fasting and abstinence established by the Church.
5. You shall help to provide for the needs of the Church.

The Corporal Works of Mercy

- Feeding the hungry
- Giving drink to the thirsty
- Clothing the naked
- Sheltering the homeless
- Visiting the sick
- Visiting the imprisoned
- Burying the dead

The Spiritual Works of Mercy

- Counseling the doubtful
- Instructing the ignorant
- Admonishing sinners
- Comforting the afflicted
- Forgiving offenses
- Bearing wrongs patiently
- Praying for the living and the dead

The Gifts of the Holy Spirit

- Wisdom
- Understanding
- Counsel
- Fortitude
- Knowledge
- Piety
- Fear of the Lord

Theological Virtues

- Faith
- Hope
- Charity

The Sins that Cry to Heaven

- The murder of the innocent (cf. Gn 4:10)
- Homosexual behavior (cf. Gn 18:20, 19:13)
- The enslavement of people (cf. Ex 3:7–10)
- Oppression of the widow, orphan, or alien (cf. Ex 22:21–24)
- Withholding wages from the laborer (cf. Dt 24:14–15)

"The catechetical tradition also recalls that there are '*sins that cry to heaven*': the blood of Abel, the sin of the Sodomites, the cry of the people oppressed in Egypt, the cry of the foreigner, the widow, and the orphan, injustice to the wage earner" (CCC 1867).

Capital Sins

- Pride
- Covetousness
- Lust
- Anger
- Gluttony
- Envy
- Sloth

Opposed Virtues

- Humility
- Liberality
- Chastity
- Meekness
- Temperance
- Brotherly love
- Diligence

Cardinal Virtues

- Prudence
- Justice
- Fortitude
- Temperance

The Beatitudes   (Mt 5:3–12)

- Blessed are the poor in spirit, for theirs is the kingdom of heaven.
- Blessed are those who mourn, for they shall be comforted.
- Blessed are the meek, for they shall inherit the earth.
- Blessed are those who hunger and thirst for righteousness, for they shall be satisfied.
- Blessed are the merciful, for they shall obtain mercy.
- Blessed are the pure of heart, for they shall see God.
- Blessed are the peacemakers, for they shall be called sons of God.
- Blessed are those who are persecuted for righteousness' sake, for theirs is the kingdom of heaven.
- Blessed are you when men revile you and persecute you and utter all kinds of evil against you falsely on my account. Rejoice and be glad, for your reward is great in heaven.

The Sign of the Cross

In the name of the Father, and of the Son, and of the Holy Spirit. Amen.

The Lord's Prayer

Our Father, who art in heaven, hallowed be thy name. Thy kingdom come; thy will be done on earth as it is in heaven. Give us this day our daily bread; and forgive us our trespasses as we forgive those who trespass against us; and lead us not into temptation, but deliver us from evil. Amen.

The Hail Mary

Hail, Mary, full of grace, the Lord is with you; blessed are you among women, and blessed is the fruit of your womb, Jesus. Holy Mary, Mother of God, pray for us sinners, now and at the hour of our death. Amen.

The Glory Be (The Doxology)

Glory be to the Father, and to the Son, and to the Holy Spirit. As it was in the beginning, is now, and ever shall be, world without end. Amen.

Morning Offering

O Jesus, through the Immaculate Heart of Mary, I offer you my prayers, works, joys, and sufferings of this day for all the intentions of your Sacred Heart, in union with the Holy Sacrifice of the Mass throughout the world, in thanksgiving for your favors, in reparation for my sins, for the intentions of all my relatives and friends, and in particular for the intentions of the Holy Father. Amen.

Consecration to the Blessed Virgin Mary

My Queen and my Mother, I give myself entirely to you, and, in proof of my affection, I give you my eyes, my ears, my tongue, my heart, my whole being without reserve. Since I am your own, keep me and guard me as your property and possession. Amen.

Act of Faith

O my God, I firmly believe that you are one God in three divine Persons, Father, Son, and Holy Spirit; I believe that your divine Son became man and died for our sins, and that he shall come to judge the living and the dead. I believe these and all the truths that the holy Catholic Church teaches, because you have revealed them, who can neither deceive nor be deceived.

Act of Hope

O my God, relying on your almighty power and infinite mercy and promises, I hope to obtain pardon for my sins, the help of your grace, and life everlasting, through the merits of Jesus Christ, my Lord and Redeemer.

Act of Charity

O my God, I love you above all things, with my whole heart and soul, because you are all-good and worthy of all love. I love my neighbor as myself for the love of you. I forgive all who have injured me and ask pardon of all whom I have injured.

Prayer to One's Guardian Angel

Angel of God, my guardian dear, to whom God's love commits me here, ever this day (night) be at my side, to light and guard, to rule and guide. Amen.

The *Angelus* *(Said outside the Easter Season)*

℣. The angel of the Lord declared unto Mary;

℟. And she conceived by the Holy Spirit.

Hail Mary...

℣. Behold the handmaid of the Lord.

℟. Be it done unto me according to your word.

Hail Mary...

℣. And the Word was made flesh,

℟. And dwelt among us.

Hail Mary...

℣. Pray for us, O holy Mother of God.

℟. That we may be made worthy of the promises of Christ.

℣. Let us pray.
Pour forth we beseech you, O Lord, your grace into our hearts, that we, to whom the Incarnation of Christ, your Son, was made known by the message of an angel, may by his Passion and Cross be brought to the glory of his Resurrection, through the same Christ our Lord.

℟. Amen.

Regina Cæli *(Said during the Easter Season)*

℣. Queen of heaven, rejoice! Alleluia.

℟. For he whom you did merit to bear. Alleluia.

℣. Has risen, as he said. Alleluia.

℟. Pray for us to God. Alleluia.

℣. Rejoice and be glad, O Virgin Mary. Alleluia.

℟. For the Lord is truly risen. Alleluia.

℣. Let us pray.
O God who gave joy to the world through the Resurrection of your Son, our Lord Jesus Christ, grant, we beseech you, that through the intercession of the Virgin Mary, his Mother, we may obtain the joys of everlasting life, through the same Christ our Lord.

℟. Amen.

Prayer to the Holy Spirit

℣. Come, O Holy Spirit, fill the hearts of your faithful and enkindle in them the fire of your love. Send forth your Spirit, and they shall be created.

℟. And you shall renew the face of the earth.

℣. Let us pray.
O God, who has taught the hearts of the faithful by the light of the Holy Spirit, grant that by the gift of the same Spirit we may be always truly wise and ever rejoice in his consolation. Through Christ our Lord.

℟. Amen

Eternal Rest

℣. Eternal rest grant unto them (him/her), O Lord,

℟. And let perpetual light shine upon them (him/her).

℣. May they (he/she) rest in peace.

℟. Amen.

℣. May their (his/her) soul(s) and the souls of all the faithful departed, through the mercy of God, rest in peace.

℟. Amen.

Blessing Before a Meal

Bless us, O Lord, and these your gifts, which we are about to receive from your bounty, through Christ our Lord. Amen.

Thanksgiving After a Meal

We give you thanks, almighty God, for all your benefits, who live and reign forever and ever. [And may the souls of the faithful departed, through the mercy of God, rest in peace.] Amen.

The Apostles' Creed

I believe in God,
the Father almighty,
Creator of heaven and earth,
and in Jesus Christ, his only Son, our Lord,
who was conceived by the Holy Spirit,
born of the Virgin Mary,
suffered under Pontius Pilate,
was crucified, died and was buried;
he descended into hell;
on the third day he rose again from the dead;
he ascended into heaven,
and is seated at the right hand
     of God the Father almighty;
from there he will come to judge
     the living and the dead.

I believe in the Holy Spirit,
the holy catholic Church,
the communion of saints,
the forgiveness of sins,
the resurrection of the body,
and life everlasting. Amen.

Fatima Prayer

O my Jesus, forgive us our sins, save us from the fire of hell, draw all souls to heaven, especially those who are in most need of your mercy. Amen.

Hail Holy Queen

Hail, holy Queen, Mother of mercy, our life, our sweetness, and our hope. To you do we cry, poor banished children of Eve. To you do we send up our sighs, mourning and weeping in this valley of tears. Turn then, most gracious Advocate, your eyes of mercy towards us, and after this exile show unto us the blessed fruit of your womb, Jesus. O clement, O loving, O sweet Virgin Mary.

℣. Pray for us, O holy Mother of God.

℟. That we may be made worthy of the promises of Christ.

Rosary Prayer

O God, whose Only-Begotten Son, by his Life, Death, and Resurrection, has purchased for us the rewards of eternal life; grant, we beseech you, that we, who meditate on these mysteries of the most holy Rosary of the Blessed Virgin Mary, may imitate what they contain, and obtain what they promise. Through Christ our Lord. Amen.

The *Memorare*

Remember, O most gracious Virgin Mary, that never was it known that anyone who fled to your protection, implored your help, or sought your intercession was left unaided. Inspired with this confidence, I fly unto you, O Virgin of virgins, my Mother. To you I come, before you I stand, sinful and sorrowful. O Mother of the Word incarnate, despise not my petitions, but in your mercy hear and answer me. Amen.

Act of Contrition

O my God, I am heartily sorry for having offended you, and I detest all my sins, because I dread the loss of heaven and the pains of hell; but most of all because they offend you, my God, who are all-good and deserving of all of my love. I firmly resolve, with the help of your grace, to confess my sins, to do penance, and to amend my life. Amen.

Prayer to St. Michael

Saint Michael the archangel, defend us in battle; be our defense against the wickedness and snares of the Devil. May God rebuke him, we humbly pray. And do you, O prince of the heavenly host, by the power of God thrust into hell Satan and all the evil spirits who prowl about the world for the ruin of souls. Amen.

How to Pray the Rosary

1. Holding the Crucifix in your hand, make the Sign of the Cross and pray the Apostles' Creed.
2. On the first bead after the Crucifix, pray the Our Father.
3. Pray one Hail Mary on each of the next three beads, asking God to increase faith, hope, and charity in your life.
4. On the bead after these three, pray the Glory Be, announce the First Mystery, and pray the Our Father.
5. Pray one Hail Mary for each of the ten following beads, and end them by praying the Glory Be and the Fatima Prayer.
6. Announce the Second Mystery and repeat steps four and five. Do the same for the Third, Fourth, and Fifth Mysteries.
7. After the Fatima Prayer for the Fifth Mystery, pray the Hail Holy Queen, the Rosary Prayer, and end with the Sign of the Cross.

The Joyful Mysteries

1. The Annunciation   (Lk 1:26–38)
2. The Visitation   (Lk 1:39–56)
3. The Nativity   (Lk 2:1–20)
4. The Presentation   (Lk 2:22–38)
5. The Finding of Jesus in the Temple   (Lk 2:41–51)

The Luminous Mysteries

1. The Baptism of Christ in the Jordan   (Mk 1:9–11)
2. The Manifestation of Christ at the Wedding of Cana   (Jn 2:1–12)
3. The Proclamation of the Kingdom of God, with His Call to Conversion   (Mk 1:14–15)
4. The Transfiguration   (Mk 9:2–8)
5. The Institution of the Eucharist   (Mk 14:22–26)

The Sorrowful Mysteries

1. The Agony in the Garden   (Mt 26:36–46)
2. The Scourging at the Pillar   (Jn 19:1)
3. The Crowning with Thorns   (Mt 27:29)
4. The Carrying of the Cross   (Jn 19:16–17)
5. The Crucifixion   (Jn 19:18–30)

The Glorious Mysteries

1. The Resurrection   (Mk 16:1–8)
2. The Ascension   (Lk 24:50–52)
3. The Descent of the Holy Spirit   (Acts 2:1–13)
4. The Assumption   (Ps 16:10)
5. The Coronation of the Blessed Virgin Mary   (Rev 12:1–2)

The Stations of the Cross

Traditional

1. Jesus Is Condemned to Death
2. Jesus Takes Up His Cross
3. Jesus Falls for the First Time
4. Jesus Meets His Blessed Mother
5. Simon of Cyrene Helps Jesus to Carry the Cross
6. Veronica Wipes the Face of Jesus
7. Jesus Falls a Second Time
8. Jesus Consoles the Women of Jerusalem
9. Jesus Falls the Third Time
10. Jesus Is Stripped of His Garments
11. Jesus Is Nailed to the Cross
12. Jesus Dies on the Cross
13. Jesus Is Laid in the Arms of His Blessed Mother
14. Jesus Is Laid in the Tomb

Biblical, of St. John Paul II

This version of the Stations of the Cross was celebrated by St. John Paul II on Good Friday, 1991.

1. Jesus in the Garden of Gethsemane   (Mt 25:36–41)
2. Jesus, Betrayed by Judas, is Arrested   (Mk 14:43–46)
3. Jesus Is Condemned by the Sanhedrin   (Lk 22:66–71)
4. Jesus Is Denied by Peter   (Mt 26:69–75)
5. Jesus Is Judged by Pilate   (Mk 15:1–5, 15)
6. Jesus Is Scourged and Crowned with Thorns   (Jn 19:1–3)
7. Jesus Bears the Cross   (Jn 19:6, 15–17)
8. Jesus Is Helped by Simon the Cyrenian to Carry the Cross   (Mk 15:21)
9. Jesus Meets the Women of Jerusalem   (Lk 23:27–31)
10. Jesus Is Crucified   (Lk 23:33–34)
11. Jesus Promises His Kingdom to the Good Thief   (Lk 23:39–43)
12. Jesus Speaks to His Mother and the Disciple   (Jn 19:25–27)
13. Jesus Dies on the Cross   (Lk 23:44–46)
14. Jesus Is Placed in the Tomb   (Mt 27:57–60)

An Overview of the Sacraments

Sacrament	Matter	Form	Minister(s)	Instituted by Christ
Baptism	water	"I baptize you in the name of the Father, and of the Son, and of the Holy Spirit."	bishop, priest, or deacon; in the case of emergency, anyone may baptize, even a non-baptized person, if the intention is to do what the Church does when she baptizes	Mt 28:19–20
Confirmation	holy chrism	"Be sealed with the gift of the Holy Spirit."	a bishop is the ordinary minister of Confirmation, although a bishop may grant the faculty to a priest	Lk 24:49 Acts 2:1–4
Eucharist	wheat bread, grape wine	"…this is my Body…this is my Blood…"	bishop or priest	Mt 26:26–29 Mk 14:22–25 Lk 22:19–20 Jn 6:35–36
Penance and Reconciliation	oral confession of sins	"…I absolve you from your sins in the Name of the Father, and of the Son, and of the Holy Spirit."	bishop or priest	Mt 16:19 Mt 18:18 Jn 20:22–23
Anointing of the Sick	oil of the sick	"Through this holy anointing, may the Lord in his love and mercy help you with the grace of the Holy Spirit. May the Lord who frees you from sin, save you and raise you up."	bishop or priest	Mk 6:13 Jas 5:14–15
Holy Orders	laying on of hands	the sacramental form is the consecratory prayer that is different for the ordination of deacon, priest, or bishop	bishop	Lk 22:19 Acts 6:6
Matrimony	the couple themselves	the vows as exchanged by the couple	the couple themselves	Mk 10:7–9 Jn 2:1–11